...ch other very much!

Laa-Laa

Po

# This Teletubbies Annual 2000 belongs to

.................Elliott Sutton.................

First published in 1999 by BBC Worldwide Ltd
Woodlands, 80 Wood Lane, London, W12 OTT
Text from original scripts by Andrew Davenport
Text, design and illustrations © 1999 BBC Worldwide Ltd
Teletubbies characters and logo © and ™ 1996 Ragdoll Productions (UK) Ltd
Licensed by BBC Worldwide Ltd

ISBN 0 563 55621 8

Written by Ruth Paley and David Moore
Designed by Daniel Rachael
Colour reproduction by Radstock Reproductions Ltd, Midsomer Norton
Printed and bound by Proost NV, Turnhout, Belgium
Illustrated by Jane Swift/SGA. Photography by Christopher Baines and Chris Capstick

Thank you to the following children who were photographed for this book:
Max, Barnaby, Bethany, Daisy-Ann, Claire, Rebecca and Paris

# Time for... Teletubbies

## Annual 2000

## Where have the Teletubbies gone?

# Tooter

**ping**

One day in Teletubbyland, something appeared from far away.

Oooh! What a funny thing!

Po, on her scooter, found a little tooter.

Ooooh, tooter!

4

Po got off her her scooter and blew the little tooter.

Blow tooter!

One, two, three... BLOW!

toot!

Po showed Laa-Laa the tooter.

One, two, three... BLOW!

toot!

Laa-Laa wanted to blow the tooter.

Ooooh, Laa-Laa blow tooter!

Laa-Laa gave the tooter a very big blow.

Very big blow!

One, two, three... BLOW!

Laa-Laa decided to give the tooter an even bigger blow.

One, two, three... BLOW!

**toot!**

The tooter tickled Tinky Winky.

**tickle! tickle!**

Tinky Winky was surprised!

Ooooh!

9

Tinky Winky wanted to blow the tooter.

Tinky Winky blow tooter!

Tinky Winky decided to give the tooter a very, very big blow.

One, two, three... BLOW!

**toot!**

The tooter tickled Dipsy.

**parp!**

**tickle!**
**tickle!**

Dipsy was surprised.

Dipsy was so surprised, he rolled all the way to the other Teletubbies.

And then the tooter disappeared.

ping

All gone!

Big Hug!

The Teletubbies love the tooter.

Teletubbies love each other very much.

11

# Making hats

You will need:
- coloured card
- safe glue
- round-ended scissors
- glitter glue
- sticky tape
- pencil

**1** Choose which Teletubby you would like to be. What colour is your Teletubby? What shape is your Teletubby's aerial?

**2** Draw a strip on some coloured card, then draw on your Teletubby's aerial shape.

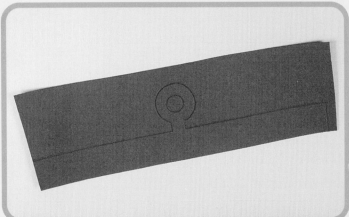

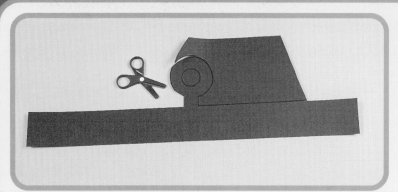

**3** Carefully cut it out using round-ended scissors.

**4** Add glitter glue to the aerial to make it look sparkly.

**5** When the glue is dry, make sure the aerial is at the back of your head and tape the two ends of the strip together.

# Colouring-in

# Ball indoors

① boing

② boing

boing

③ boing

boing

boing

**Look at the pictures and tell the story.**

# Favourite things

The Teletubbies are playing with their favourite things. Sing their songs with them!

Bup-a-tum
Bup-a-tum

Laa-laa-li-laa
Laa-laa-li-laa

What an
awful racket!

Pinkle winkle Tinky Winky Pinkle winkle Tinky Winky

Find these little pictures in the big picture. Shout "SNAP" when you find them!

Fi-dit fi-dit Fi-dit fi-dit

19

# Time for Tubby counting

## How many can you count? Draw a ring round the answer!

dancing bear

1 2 3 4 5

animals

1 2 3 4 5

Trace over the numbers with your finger!

1 2

ships

1
2
3
4
5

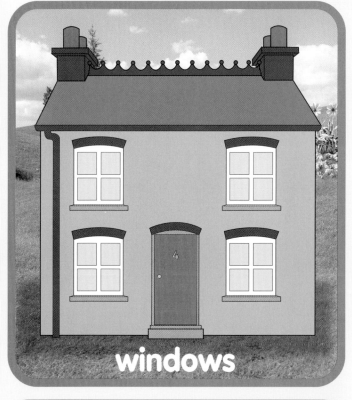

windows

1 2 3 4 5

birds

1 2 3 4 5

# Curtains

One day in Teletubbyland, something appeared from far away.

What's that?

It was a pair of curtains.

Oooh, curtains!

The curtains opened.

Open!

The curtains closed.

Closed!

Dipsy went behind the curtains.

The curtains opened.

Open!

The curtains closed.

Closed!

The curtains opened again.

Open!

The curtains closed again.

Closed! Oh no!

Laa-Laa saw the curtains.

Oooooooh!

Somebody was behind the curtains.

Who's behind the curtains?

Who's behind the curtains?

The curtains
opened.

Open!

Laa-Laa!

Big Hug!

Dipsy!

The curtains
closed.

Uh-oh!

And then – the curtains disappeared.

Dipsy and Laa-Laa love the curtains.

Teletubbies love each other very much.

**The Teletubbies are being very noisy! Join in with the Teletubbies and make all the funny noises.**

bing

bing

bong

splish

splash

splosh

boing

boing

Join up the dots and colour in Laa-Laa's ball.

Who is eating tubby toast?
Who is eating tubby custard?

29

# Come and see...

Hello! Come and see our party.

We play musical bumps. We have to dance to the music.

When the music stops we all fall down with a bump. We like this game!

Now we're going to have some special party food.

We like the cake best. Yum! Bye-bye!

Again! Again, again!

# Colouring-in

# Laa-Laa's lovely song

One day in Teletubbyland, Laa-Laa was going to sing a lovely song to Dipsy and Po.

Laa-Laa sing lovely song now.

crunch!

crunch! munch!

What's that noise?

Tinky Winky, you must not crunch your tubby toast when Laa-Laa is going to sing.

Tinky Winky listen!

Tinky Winky finished his toast, then he went to listen to Laa-Laa's lovely song.

Laa-Laa started her lovely song again.

Lovely song, a lovely song, a lovely song, a lovely song, a lovely song, a lovely song, a lovely song, a lovely so-o-o-ong!

Laa-Laa had sung such a lovely song,
that Tinky Winky, Dipsy and Po had
gone to sleep!

37

# Diddle diddle dumpling

**Again again!**

Diddle diddle dumpling, my son
One sock off and one sock on

A voice trumpet has brought a rhyme to Teletubbyland.

The Teletubbies think the rhyme is very funny. Can you say the rhyme to the Teletubbies again?

What makes you laugh?

Diddle diddle diddle!

John, went to bed with his trousers on.

diddle diddle dumpling, my son John.

39

# Tubby footsteps

Help the Noo-noo tidy up by following the trail of tubby footsteps with your finger. Who has made such a mess?

**Uh-oh!**

# The Lion and the Bear

I am the scary Lion and
I'm looking for the Bear
I know she's hiding
But I don't know where.

I'm looking over here
and I'm looking over there
Can you see her?
Where's the Bear?

**The Lion and the Bear are playing a hiding game. Join in with the rhyme. Draw a wavy line from the Lion to the Bear – go round and round the flowers.**

# I'm a little teapot

I'm a little teapot,
Short and stout.

Here's my handle,
Here's my spout.

I'm a little teapot,
Hear me shout!

Tip me up,
And pour me out!

44

# Sing the song and do the actions for the Teletubbies!

Again!
Again, again!

I'm a little teapot, Short and stout.
Here's my handle, Here's my spout.
I'm a little teapot, Hear me shout!
Tip me up, And pour me out!

# Busy Teletubbies

○ Can you find something orange?

○ Can you find something shaped like a triangle?

○ Can you find Tinky Winky's bag?

○ Can you find somebody who is red?

○ Can you find somebody who is green?

○ Can you find Po's scooter?

○ Can you find three rabbits?

○ Can you find a pattern like this?

Very busy!

The Teletubbies are very busy.
You can be busy too! Tick a circle
when you can answer a question.

47

## Look at the pictures and tell the story.

**1**

**2**

**4**

**5**

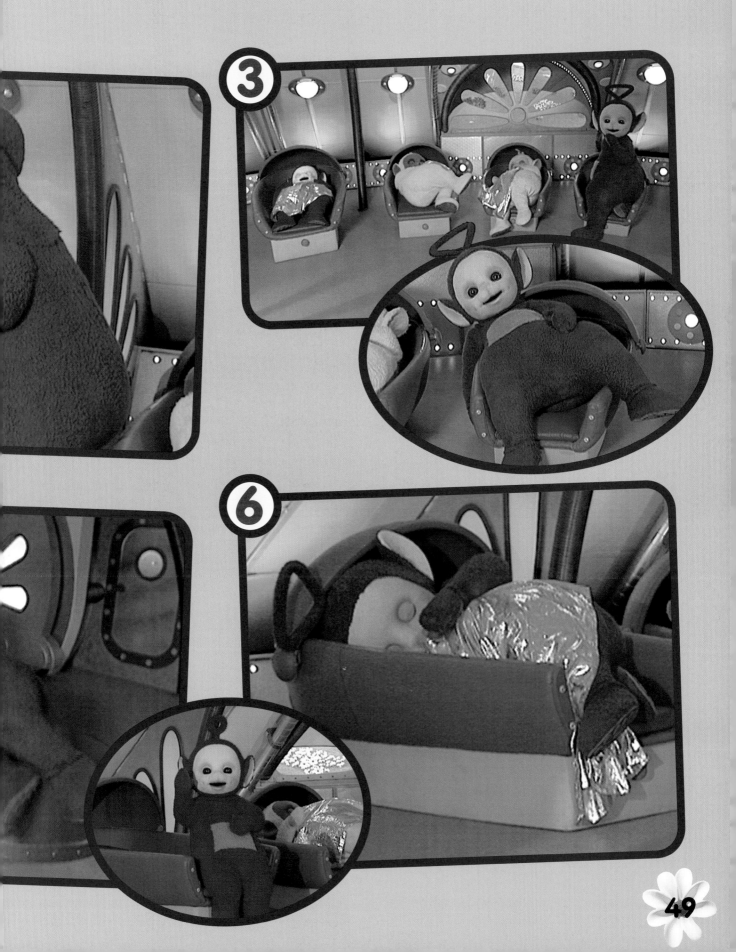

# Colouring-in

# Tubby dreams

One day in Teletubbyland the Teletubbies were dreaming. What were they dreaming about? Draw it in!

# Supposed to be in bed

One day in Teletubbyland, all the Teletubbies were feeling very tired.

So they decided to go to bed.

Go to sleep Teletubbies, go to sleep.

There.

All the Teletubbies are asleep.

Tinky Winky, Dipsy, Laa-Laa and Po.

All asleep.

Wait a minute! Where's Po?

Po is riding her scooter

Po is supposed to be in bed.

Uh-oh!

55

Go to sleep Teletubbies, go to sleep.

There. All the Teletubbies are asleep.

Tinky Winky, Dipsy, Laa-Laa and Po.

All asleep.

Wait a minute! Where's Laa-Laa?

Uh-oh!

Laa-Laa is playing with her ball.

Laa-Laa is supposed to be in bed.

There.
All the Teletubbies are asleep.

Tinky Winky, Dipsy, Laa-Laa and Po.

All asleep.

Go to sleep Teletubbies, go to sleep.

Wait a minute! Where's Dipsy?

Dipsy has gone for a walk in his hat.

Dipsy is supposed to be in bed.

Uh-oh!

Go to sleep Teletubbies, go to sleep.

There. All the Teletubbies are asleep.

Tinky Winky, Dipsy, Laa-Laa and Po.

All asleep.

Wait a minute! Where's Tinky Winky?

Uh-oh!

Tinky Winky is playing jumping with his bag.

Tinky Winky is supposed to be in bed.

Go to sleep Teletubbies, go to sleep.

There.
All the Teletubbies are asleep.

Tinky Winky, Dipsy, Laa-Laa and Po.

All asleep.

Wait a minute!
Where have all the Teletubbies gone?

The Teletubbies are supposed to be in bed!

Teletubbies love their favourite things.

And Teletubbies love each other very much.

59

# Goodbye game

Time for tubby bye-bye! Play this fun game and be the first to say "bye-bye" to the Teletubbies.

Share the skirt. Dance forward three!

**3**

**4**

**5**

boing

**2**

boing

Laa-Laa's ball! Bounce forward two!

**1**

start

Time for tubby bye-bye!

Bye-bye!

**25**

Help Tinky Winky find the bag. Go back three.

Where bag?

**24**

**23**

**22**